BOOK D

CLUES
FOR BETTER WRITING

James Flood, Diane Lapp, Nancy Farnan, Linda Lungren

Illustrated by Peter Bianco

Product Development—Robert G. Forest

Curriculum Associates

ISBN 1-55915-213-3

©1992—Curriculum Associates, Inc.
North Billerica, MA 01862

15 14 13 12 11 10 9 8 7 6 5 4 3

TABLE OF CONTENTS

Dear Student,

Welcome to the wonderful world of writing. You are about to begin a writing program that has been designed especially for young writers. It is called *Clues for Better Writing*. The program is filled with information and activities that will help you become a better writer. Writing is an important way to share your ideas with others. Think about all the books, magazines, movies, games, and television shows that you enjoy. They were written by people who were once students like you. We have written this program to help young writers like you become as successful as your favorite authors. We hope you enjoy this program and become the best writer you can be.

At this time, we would like to introduce you to Angela. You will find her picture next to this letter. Angela is a friend of young writers. She will travel with you from lesson to lesson. Angela knows a lot about writing, and she will share many good writing ideas with you. However, you must remember that Angela has one problem. She gets lost easily. Fortunately, you will have an opportunity to find Angela each time she gets lost. We provide the clues to help you in your search.

So, if you're ready for an enjoyable adventure in writing, *Clues for Better Writing* is the program for you. Be prepared to have fun as you become a better writer!

Sincerely,

James Flood

Diane Lapp

Nancy Farnan

Linda Lungren

5

Potato Skins and Paper Clips

According to Angela, inventors and writers are very much alike. Inventors put materials together to create gadgets and machines, while writers put words together to create stories and articles.

The paragraph that follows tells about a young inventor. As you read, think about the things you might invent, if given the opportunity.

My brother Dan is quite an inventor. Once he made a machine that turned off the bedroom light as soon as he jumped into bed. It's too bad Dad tripped over the machine and broke it when he came in to say goodnight to Dan one night. Last week Dan invented an automatic speed slicer that cuts vegetables in record time. Mom said the machine needs to get the potato skins and carrot tops into the garbage and not on the kitchen ceiling. I guess Dan still has a ways to go before he's famous!

What is the main idea of the paragraph? _____

_____

In which sentence did you find the main idea? _____

If you wrote that the main idea is that Dan is quite an inventor, you are correct. The main idea appears in the first sentence. The other sentences in the paragraph tell about Dan and his inventions. Now read the following paragraph about the moon. As you read, think about how much the invention of the telescope has contributed to human knowledge of the moon.

As you look at the moon through a telescope, you can see mountain ranges. Some of the mountains are more than two miles high. Deep valleys, wide craters, and flat areas, called seas, cover the moon. The surface is dry, so these seas contain no water. The moon's outer crust is made of hard, thick rock. Look closely at the moon and you will see that it has a very interesting surface.

What is the main idea of this paragraph? _____

_____

In which sentence did you find the main idea? _____

If you wrote that the main idea is that the moon has an interesting surface, you are correct. All the sentences in the paragraph tell about the surface of the moon.

Where's Angela?
Clue: *You will find her, more or less, helping to clean up the mess.*

WRITER'S CORNER

Brainstorming
Thingamajigs and Thingamabobs

- floating soap—invented by Harley Procter and James Gamble at their soap and candle factory in 1879
- roller skates—invented by a Belgian musical instrument maker, Joseph Merlin, in 1759
- blue jeans—invented by Levi Strauss during the San Francisco gold rush in the early 1850s
- can opener—invented by Ezra Warner of Waterbury, Connecticut, in 1858

Writer's Word Bank
1. current
2. organ
3. diamond
4. tablet
5. clipper
6. gear

Planning

Choose an invention to write a paragraph about. You may write about an existing invention or one of your own inventions. Perhaps you would like to write about one of the inventions listed in Thingamajigs and Thingamabobs. The choice is yours. Go to the library to find out how one of these inventions came about. (You may use words from the Writer's Word Bank.)

CLUES TO USE
- The main idea is the most important idea in a paragraph.
- The main idea may appear in the first sentence or the last sentence of the paragraph.

Plan your writing on the lines below.

Main idea: _____

_____

Notes: _____

_____

_____

Writing

On the lines below, write a paragraph about an invention and how the invention came about. Write your main idea in the first or last sentence.

_____

_____

_____

_____

_____

_____

Editing

Check to be sure that the first or last sentence contains the main idea. Then be sure the other sentences in the paragraph tell about the main idea. If one or more sentences do not tell about the main idea, rewrite the sentences.

MAIN IDEA

Sharing

Write your final copy on a separate piece of paper. Then illustrate your invention. Mount both your final copy and illustration on a piece of construction paper. Your teacher will tell you when to share your writing and illustration with your classmates.

ON YOUR OWN

Now it's your turn to write a paragraph about an idea of your choice. It can be about a *real* thing or an *imaginary* thing, a *useful* thing or a *useless* thing, a *modern* thing or an *ancient* thing. The choice is yours. In My Word Bank, write four important words you will use in your writing. (If you need help thinking of an idea to write about, check the Topic Ideas on page 106.) Write your paragraph on the lines below.

My Word Bank
1. _____
2. _____
3. _____
4. _____

_____

_____

_____

_____

_____

_____

_____

_____

_____

_____

_____

_____

Building Character

Good writers know that if they can describe the feelings that people feel, they can create characters that their readers will enjoy. (When Angela writes, she tries to create characters that seem as real as "the people next door.")

Have you ever had to do something you didn't want to do? Do you remember how you felt? Read the paragraph that follows. As you read, think about Ricky, how he feels, and how the author uses words to make him a realistic and an interesting character.

The sky was blue, but Ricky didn't seem to notice. The sun was shining, but not in the shadows where Ricky walked. This was not a day in which the bright side of life could change Ricky's mood. No matter how the world appeared, Ricky could see only darkness. His violin case felt as though it were filled with rocks instead of a violin. His head hurt, and he was already worn out by the three-block walk from the bus stop. There was one more block before he would reach Ms. Shimizu's house. He walked slowly, although he knew Ms. Shimizu was waiting for him. As usual, he was dreading his violin lesson.

What is the main idea of the paragraph? _____

_____

In which sentence did you find the main idea? _____

_____

If you noted that the main idea is that Ricky was dreading his violin lesson, you are correct. The main idea appears in the last sentence. The other sentences tell how Ricky felt about the violin lesson. The author uses the "darkness" of Ricky's mood and the "heaviness" of the violin case to create an interesting character. Ricky is like a million other kids around the country who dread music lessons; in fact, he's much like the "kid who lives next door." The author uses words in a creative way to make Ricky come to life as a person whom readers will care about.

*W*RITER'S CORNER

Brainstorming
Situations Most Kids Could Do Without

- cleaning a junk-filled garage
- visiting the dentist because of a toothache
- staying after school every afternoon for a week
- being challenged to a fight by a bully

Planning

Choose an interesting character to write about. You may choose a real or an imaginary character. Place the character in a dreadful situation. You may use one of the ideas suggested in Situations Most Kids Could Do Without. Or you may choose a dreadful situation that you recently experienced. The choice is yours. Develop your character in a way similar to the way the author developed Ricky's character—by showing what your character is doing, thinking, and feeling. (You may use words from the Writer's Word Bank.)

CLUES TO USE

- The main idea may be written in the first sentence or the last sentence of the paragraph.
- Sometimes the main idea is not directly told. The writer lets the reader figure out the main idea from the details in the paragraph.

Plan your writing on the lines below.

Main idea: _____

_____

Notes: _____

_____

_____

Writing

On the lines below, write a short paragraph about a character experiencing a dreadful situation. Then draw a picture on art paper to illustrate your character in the situation you wrote about. Be sure that the character you draw looks like the charracter you wrote about.

_____

_____

_____

_____

_____

_____

_____

Editing

Check to be sure that the main idea is obvious. Is your character interesting enough? Have you clearly described the situation that your character must deal with? If your paragraph needs other ideas to make the character more interesting, go back and make the changes. (Angela will change even her shopping list if it's not interesting enough.)

Sharing

Write your final copy on a separate piece of paper. Mount your final copy and the illustration on a large piece of construction paper. Your teacher will tell you when to share your character and the illustration with your classmates.

ON YOUR OWN

There are many wonderful characters in the books you read. Choose one character you like and write a letter to a friend about that character. Develop your letter from information given in the book. Tell about the character as if he or she were a personal acquaintance of yours. Tell your friend how you met the character. Then use precise words to draw a clear picture of the character. Don't reveal the character's name. Read your letter to the class and see if your classmates can guess the character you have described. In My Word Bank, write four important words you will use in your letter. Write your letter on the lines below.

My Word Bank
1. _____
2. _____
3. _____
4. _____

_____

_____

_____

_____

_____

_____

_____

_____

_____

_____

_____

_____

_____

Building the Writer's Word Power

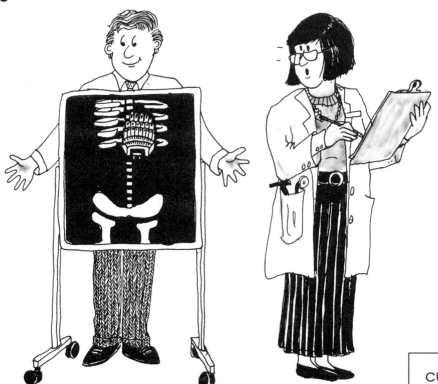

current
organ
diamond
tablet
clipper
gear

A. *Double Meaning*

Word meaning is important to writers. When using words with more than one meaning, careful writers make sure that the correct meaning is always clear.

Write words from the box to complete each sentence.

1. Each young writer was given a _____ of writing paper.

2. The _____ ship was built for great speed.

3. A baseball _____ contains four bases.

4. The ocean _____ brings warm water to Cape Cod.

5. The sailor stored his _____ in a canvas bag.

6. The heart is an important _____ in your body.

Think of another meaning for each word in the box. On a separate piece of paper, write another sentence for each word. You may use a dictionary to find new meanings.

B. Many Words, One Word

Careful writers use only words that are important to the story. There is no place for unnecessary words. Writers try not to use several words when one word will do the job.

Read each pair of sentences. In the second sentence, write the adjective from the box that best completes the sentence.

| exhausted |
| frantic |
| moist |
| countless |
| mournful |
| ridiculous |

1. Davy Crockett encountered an enormous number of bears.

   Davy Crockett encountered _____ bears.

2. Paul Bunyan was deeply worried and desperately concerned about Blue Ox's disappearance.

   Paul Bunyan was _____ about Blue Ox's disappearance.

3. Sluefoot Sue found herself in a silly and laughable situation.

   Sluefoot Sue found herself in a _____ situation.

4. John Henry was worn out and tired after digging the tunnel.

   John Henry was _____ after digging the tunnel.

5. Pocahontas heard a cry from John Smith that was filled with grief.

   Pocahontas heard John Smith's _____ cry.

6. Johnny Appleseed planted each seed in soil that was wet with water.

   Johnny Appleseed planted each seed in _____ soil.

Being Particular

A Sign of the Times

Every day of your life, you come across signs reminding you to do or not to do things. Have you noticed how much of the environment is scattered with signs? Some of these signs give brief, simple commands.

Do not enter.	**Keep off the grass.**	**Use other exit.**

Other signs are somewhat more elaborate. Read the two signs below that appeared in a camping area. As you read each sign, think about its main idea. Then decide if each sentence in the sign supports that main idea.

Beware of Black Bears!

Black bears have been returning to these woods during the last year. Most of them do not like people. Black bears can be dangerous, so use caution! Food attracts bears, so do not keep food in your tent. Do not leave food outside your car at night unless you hang the food by a rope from a tree branch.

Protect Yourself from Snakes!

There are at least twenty-seven different kinds of snakes in these woods. Do not leave your tent flap open at any time. When hiking, carry a long, forked stick and wear thick-soled leather boots.

WRITING DETAILS

The camping signs tell readers a lot in a few sentences.

What brings bears to camp areas? _____

_____

Why do some hikers carry long, forked sticks? _____

_____

The main idea of each sign appears in the title. Both main ideas are warnings. The sentences that follow each title give details that support the main idea. These sentences tell campers *why* they should obey the warning. What are some other warnings that might be the main ideas of signs in

camping areas? _____

Where's Angela?
Clue: *Angela's serving near a group. Look and find her near the soup.*

WRITER'S CORNER

Brainstorming
More Warning Signs
- Bathers: Avoid Hours in the Sun
- Smokers: Cigarettes Are Hazardous to Your Health
- Dieters: Reduce Daily Intake of Fats
- Pedestrians: Cross at Crosswalks

Writer's Word Bank
1. stroll
2. personal
3. purchase
4. education
5. challenge
6. style

Planning

Decide on a warning sign to create. The sign may be based on a familiar warning, such as one of the warnings above. Or you may plan your warning sign around an idea of your own. After you determine the main idea, consider the important details that readers of your sign must pay attention to. (You may use words from the Writer's Word Bank.)

CLUES TO USE
- Writers use details to tell more about the main idea.
- Details make a story (or sign) more interesting to read.

Plan your writing on the lines below.

Main idea: _____

_____

Important details: _____

_____

_____

Writing

On the lines below, write your warning sign.

_____

_____

_____

_____

_____

_____

_____

_____

_____

_____

Editing

Check to be sure that you have included details that are important to the readers of your sign. Did you provide a reason for the warning sign? If you did not, go back and make the necessary changes.

Sharing

On art paper, print the final copy of your warning sign. Work carefully so that your sign looks like an actual sign. You may also wish to include an illustration. Mount your finished sign on the classroom wall to share with your classmates.

WRITING DETAILS

ON YOUR OWN

Angela says it's time for you to create a different kind of warning sign. Think of a favorite story character that could have been helped by a warning sign. Pick a surprising situation in the story that was difficult for your character. Create a warning sign to help the character prepare for the situation. For example, Ann Shirley of *Anne of Green Gables* would have been better prepared to handle Marilla Cuthbert if Anne had read a warning sign before entering the Cuthbert home.

My Word Bank
1. _____
2. _____
3. _____
4. _____

Beware! Enter the Cuthbert Home with Caution!

Marilla Cuthbert has a one-track mind and can be very difficult to deal with. She plans to adopt a child to help with the chores. She is determined that the child be a boy. Girls need not enter here.

Read the contents of your warning sign to your classmates. Do not reveal the character. Ask your classmates to name the character that would be helped by the warning sign. In My Word Bank, write four important words you will use as you write your sign. Write your sign on the lines below.

_____

_____

_____

_____

_____

_____

_____

_____

_____

Now Hear This!

Sometimes writing a letter is the best way to be heard. Good writers know that well-written letters have a way of getting the attention of the reader. (Angela recently wrote a letter of complaint to a department store and got an immediate reply. She was invited to shop at another store.)

Sometimes writers use letters as part of the story line to develop the plot. These letters often provide details that help readers enjoy the story more fully. A copy of the first half of Felicity Lawson's letter to Ethel Hurley, editor of the *Early Tribune,* is reprinted below. As you read the letter, think about Felicity's reason for writing.

---

121 Purview Drive
Phelps, New York 14532
March 3, 1991

Ethel Hurley, Editor
Early Tribune
Phelps, New York 14532

Dear Ms. Hurley:

   You have a good newspaper, but you're missing one important thing. You should have more news about the Truman Elementary School. Exciting things happen here at the Truman School. There are book fairs, plays, sporting events, and sometimes even magic shows. Besides, if you had more news about the Truman School, all the kids from the school and their parents would want to read the Early Tribune. Your newspaper sales would increase. Also, it would make Mr. Chang, our principal, very proud to read about his school in his favorite newspaper.

                    Sincerely,

                    Felicity Lawson

Why do you think Felicity wrote the letter? _____

_____

If your answer is "to ask the editor to print more news about Truman Elementary School," you are correct. In fact, this answer is also the main idea of the paragraph. Now think about the supporting details in the paragraph.

Supporting details may answer questions such as WHO, WHAT, WHERE, WHEN, and WHY. However, all questions are seldom answered in a single paragraph. Study the following chart about the letter you just read.

WHO	Mrs. Hurley, editor at the *Early Tribune*
WHAT	print the exciting things that happen
WHERE	at the Truman Elementary School
WHEN	(no specific detail given)
WHY	newspaper sales would increase; Mr. Chang would be proud to read about his school

WRITER'S CORNER

Brainstorming
Mr. Lipp's Detail Chart

WHO	Mr. Lipp, a retired trumpet player
WHAT	refused to pay the bill
WHERE	at the Driftwood Restaurant
WHEN	around 7:00 P.M. on Tuesday evening
WHY	because he found a fly in his soup

Writer's Word Bank
1. praise
2. explode
3. amuse
4. snarl
5. mutter
6. knead

Planning

Plan to write a letter to a friend. In your letter, describe an amusing incident that occurred recently. Perhaps you would like to write about Mr. Lipp and the incident that occurred at dinner one evening at a local restaurant. If so, look back at Mr. Lipp's Detail Chart. Perhaps you would like to write about another person and incident. The choice is yours. However, if you choose another person, complete the detail chart before you begin to write. (You may use words from the Writer's Word Bank.)

<table>
<tr><td colspan="2" align="center">CLUES TO USE</td></tr>
<tr><td colspan="2">• Writers use details to tell more about the main idea.
• Details may explain the WHO, WHAT, WHERE, WHEN, and WHY of the main idea.</td></tr>
</table>

Plan your friendly letter about an amusing incident on the chart below.

WHO	
WHAT	
WHERE	
WHEN	
WHY	

Writing

On the lines below and on the next page, write a friendly letter telling about an amusing incident. Use the correct format for a friendly letter. Find or draw a picture to illustrate the incident.

_____

_____

_____

_____

_____

_____

_____

_____

_____

_____

_____

_____

_____

_____

_____

_____

_____

Editing

Check your letter to be sure that you have included details about the five *W*'s: WHO, WHAT, WHEN, WHERE, and WHY. If the details need to be changed, go back and write details that improve your letter.

Sharing

Write the final copy of your letter on a separate piece of paper. Mount the final copy and the illustration together on art paper. Your teacher will tell you when to share your letter with your classmates.

ON YOUR OWN

Given a choice, some students prefer to write about their own ideas. You may be one of those students. (Angela certainly is!) Now is the time for you to write a story about any idea you wish. Write your story on a separate piece of paper. Then illustrate your story on art paper. In My Word Bank, write four important words you will use in your writing. (If you need help thinking of an idea to write about, check the Topic Ideas on page 106.) Share your story and illustration with your classmates.

My Word Bank
1. _____
2. _____
3. _____
4. _____

Building the Writer's Word Power

A. *Wacky Words*

Writers enjoy word games. Use each Wacky Word Clue to fill in the Wacky Phrase beside it. Then complete the definition with a word from the box. The first Wacky Word Phrase has been solved for you.

> stroll
> personal
> purchase
> education
> challenge
> style

Wacky Word Clue	Wacky Word Phrase	Definition
1. SCHOOL	High School	a place to get an _____
2. deer (diamond sign)	_____ _____	road area where deer _____
3. CÓÚNTÈR	_____-_____ _____	place to pay for items you_____
4. house	_____-_____ _____	a _____ of house
5. pAINS	_____ _____	problems at the start of a new_____
6. GOSSIP (vertical)	_____ _____	a newspaper section that includes _____ news

Invent Wacky Word Clues of your own. Ask other students to solve them.

| praise |
| explode |
| amuse |
| snarl |
| mutter |
| knead |

B. *Action Words*

Action stories are often filled with verbs that draw clear pictures of the action.

On each line below, write the verb from the box that means the same as the underlined words.

1. I heard the teacher <u>say wonderful things about</u> them. _____

2. Bakers <u>press, squeeze, and stretch</u> the dough. _____

3. Clowns can <u>make</u> us <u>laugh</u>. _____

4. Some dogs <u>growl and bare their teeth</u>. _____

5. Fireworks <u>burst open with a loud noise</u>. _____

6. Actors should not <u>speak unclearly in low tones</u>. _____

Detectives at Work

Looking for Clues

Most readers work like detectives. Good readers are meticulous, paying attention to each detail. They carefully look for information to help them understand. As they read, they gather clues and put those clues together to figure out what happened or to predict what is going to happen. A meticulous writer provides the reader with many helpful clues. Read the following passage about an inventor. Gather clues from the illustration and the passage to see if you can predict what the invention will be. (Angela insists that meticulous readers find good clues in illustrations, too.)

Prisoner William Addis is trying to think of new ways of earning money when he is set free. Suddenly, as he is getting himself ready in the morning, Addis has an idea for a useful tool. (The year is 1770.)

Write your prediction. _____

_____

You may have found that predicting what the invention will be is difficult because of the lack of details. Maybe you need more specific information. Read the rewritten passage.

Prisoner William Addis is trying to think of new ways of earning money when he is set free. Suddenly, as he is cleaning his teeth with a rag, Addis has an idea for a useful tool.

What major detail has been added? _____

_____

Use the new information to predict what the invention is. _____

_____

PREDICTING OUTCOMES

If you figured out that the invention is a toothbrush, you are correct. You have correctly put the clues together to build your understanding. This is what readers do when they read. Now you know why it's important for writers to provide good clues when they write.

Where's Angela?

Clue: *A picnic is the place to be. You'll find Angela in a shady tree.*

WRITER'S CORNER

Brainstorming
Seen at the Scene

- Scene: a picnic
  Clue: a feather beside a half-eaten hamburger
- Scene: a spelling test
  Clue: a list of spelling words on the floor beside a student
- Scene: a bakery
  Clue: an annoyed cook speaking to a child who has crumbs on his face
- Scene: a house
  Clue: footprints in the snow leading away from a broken window

Writer's Word Bank
1. sparrow
2. request
3. tailor
4. orchard
5. nephew
6. racket

Planning

Choose a topic for a short mystery story. As you think about the plot, plan to include two or more clues (details) to help the reader figure out what is happening or to hint at what will happen next. Perhaps you would like to write about a topic suggested in Seen at the Scene. The choice is yours. Remember to provide at least two clues. (You may use words from the Writer's Word Bank.)

CLUES TO USE

- Writers use story clues to help readers predict outcomes.
- Writers include details that help readers understand what is happening.

Plan your writing on the lines below.

The topic: _____

_____

Story clues: _____

_____

_____

Writing

On the lines below and on the next page, write a short mystery story using story clues.

_____

_____

_____

_____

_____

_____

_____

_____

_____

_____

_____

_____

_____

_____

_____

_____

Editing

Check to be sure that your short story contains clues that help readers understand what is happening. Is your story interesting enough? If not, go back and rewrite the clues.

Sharing

Your teacher will tell you when to share your short story with the class. Before you read, ask your classmates to listen and write down the clues they hear that reveal what is happening in the story. Review the clues after the reading and discuss any missed clues.

●N YOUR OWN

The name of the activity is What (or Who) Am I? Choose a mystery topic. On a separate piece of paper, write the topic and six super clues about the topic. Read the clues one at a time to your classmates. After each clue is presented, ask your classmates to write down what or who they think your topic is. Then read the next clue. Ask them again to guess in writing. Continue this procedure until all the clues are read. Then reveal the mystery "what" or "who." Find out which classmates guessed correctly. Ask which clue helped the most. In My Word Bank, write four important words you will use in writing your clues.

My Word Bank

1. _____

2. _____

3. _____

4. _____

Detectives at Work

L e s s o n **8**

What Goes Up Must Come Down

Good writers provide clues that help readers piece story ideas together. Read the selection that follows. At each step in the reading, predict what you think is about to happen. Use the story clues to guide your predictions. (Angela enjoys making predictions. It makes reading enjoyable.)

Coming Down!

1. From the title, what might the story be about? _____
_____

Rita and Carlos were very still as they stood in front of their apartment house. They were looking up at the balcony of the apartment on the top floor.

"I see it," Rita whispered. "They've got it out—it's on the balcony!"

Two men stood across the street. In their hands they held a rope that hung down from the top of the building.

2. What do you think is going to happen? _____
_____

"Okay, Marley," one of the men called. "Put a strap around it—under its belly." At the sound of the animal's cry, the man shouted, "No! You've pulled the strap too tight!"

3. Have your predictions changed? _____ Why or why not? _____
_____

"I don't see Mom," Carlos said, still looking up.

Rita didn't answer him. Instead she cried, "Oh, look! It's scared. It keeps shaking its mane. Poor dear. Oh, I'm so sorry. Forgive me, please!"

4. Now what do you think is going to happen? _____
_____

PREDICTING OUTCOMES

5. What story clues helped you make this prediction? _____

_____

6. Discuss all the possibilities that the clues suggest. Go back and check to see if the clues support each prediction. What do you and your classmates think is the most important clue the author has provided up to this point?

_____

7. What will happen next? _____

_____

Your teacher will tell you how the author ends the story.

WRITER'S CORNER

Brainstorming
Animal Crackers

- elephant—trunk, huge ears, tusks—can be trained to dance and play baseball
- giraffe—very tall, long legs, long neck—can close its nostrils completely to help keep out sand
- penguin—black and white bird, stands upright, waddles—cannot fly but is a superb swimmer

Writer's Word Bank
1. faithful
2. honest
3. tender
4. awkward
5. patient
6. cautious

Planning

Choose an animal to write a poem about. You may write about one of the animals listed in Animal Crackers or about an animal of your choice. Research your animal in the library. Build your poem by inserting clues along the way. (You may use words from the Writer's Word Bank.) Do not reveal the name of your animal. Study the following poem model and note the two-line rhyming pattern.

> I saw a bird that cannot fly.
>
> And when it walks, it waddles by.
>
> Its flipper wings help it to be
>
> The swimming champ of the ice-cold sea.

CLUES TO USE

- Writers use clues to help readers understand what is happening in a poem or a story.
- Writers provide clues to help readers predict outcomes.

Plan your poem on the lines below.

_____

_____

_____

_____

Writing

On the lines below, write your mystery animal poem. Use rhyme for each pair of lines.

_____

_____

_____

_____

_____

_____

Editing

Check to be sure that your poem has a regular beat, or rhythm. Does each pair of lines rhyme? Have you included clues that will help readers determine the mystery animal? If not, go back and make the necessary changes.

Sharing

Your teacher will tell you when to read your poem to your classmates. At the end of the reading, ask your classmates to identify the animal.

ON YOUR OWN

Everyone is concerned about the weather. People plan their lives around the weather. Sometimes the weather can be pleasant, while other times it can be unpleasant or even violent. Write a short description about a violent form of weather, such as a hurricane, a dust storm, or a blizzard. Provide clues that help readers predict what will happen as you develop your description. In My Word Bank, write four important words you will use in your writing. Write your description on the lines below.

My Word Bank

1. _____

2. _____

3. _____

4. _____

_____

_____

_____

_____

_____

_____

_____

_____

_____

_____

Building the Writer's Word Power

| sparrow |
| request |
| tailor |
| orchard |
| nephew |
| racket |

A. *We're Related*

Writers often use related words to make their stories interesting.

Write a word from the box to complete each relationship.

1. *aunt* is to *uncle* as *niece* is to _____

2. *golf* is to *club* as *tennis* is to _____

3. *tell* is to *ask* as *declare* is to _____

4. *grape* is to *vineyard* as *apple* is to _____

5. *fish* is to *trout* as *bird* is to _____

6. *hammer* is to *carpenter* as *needle* is to _____

B. *Add-on Words*

When writers use verbs to describe actions, they often include other words that help the reader picture the action more clearly. These words are called *adverbs*. Many adverbs are made by adding *ly* to adjectives.

faithful
honest
tender
awkward
patient
cautious

Add *ly* to an adjective in the box to make an adverb that best completes each sentence. Use each word only once.

1. The hikers approached the ledge _____ .

2. The passengers waited _____ for the driver to return.

3. The thief insisted that he had answered all questions _____ .

4. Her dog always walked _____ by her side.

5. The clown stumbled _____ and bumped into the wall.

6. Angela cuddled the baby _____ .

Place Settings

Writers help readers draw conclusions about what they read. When readers draw conclusions, they make judgments or form ideas about someone or something in the story. Their conclusions are based on story clues, facts, and details that the writer has provided. (Angela draws conclusions better than she draws pictures.)

Read the three journal entries. What conclusions can you draw from the information that is given?

The Voyage of the *Carter Jameson*

November 14. We left Nantucket under a gray sky. Many of our friends came down to the dock to send us off. How sad it is not knowing if I will ever see those friends again on earth. Allison did not share her mother's sorrow. She quickly ran down to the crew's quarters and discovered that there was a monkey on board.

November 28. Nothing but high seas and dark skies for days. Eating continues to be a painful duty. I asked Captain Murray to replace our cook before we're all dead. Allison, still in high spirits, begged to be allowed on deck in the storm. I have to keep an eye on her at all times.

December 12. Today we began our meals under a new cook (the third so far). Breakfast was the only meal I could eat. The cooking is still very poor. Captain Murray agreed, judging by the food left on his plate. However, all worries are now gone as the men have since raised a school of whales. This seems a good omen for the voyage. Everywhere one can see smiles where before there were only frowns.

The setting of a story is where the story takes place. The writer of this journal does not state directly where she is. However, she provides plenty of clues from which you can draw your own conclusion as to where the story is taking place. What is the setting for the journal writer's adventure?

What clues tell you this? _____

_____

A major concern for the journal writer seems to be the food. What clues help

the reader draw this conclusion? _____

_____

_____

Sometimes readers compare story events with their own experiences. What events in the journal can you compare with an experience you once had? Explain how your experience and the writer's were similar.

_____

_____

Where's Angela?
Clue: If you look where pirates go, Angela will wave a fond "hello."

WRITER'S CORNER

Brainstorming
Sensational Story Settings
- a mountain cabin during a blizzard
- the seashore during a hurricane
- a busy highway during a police chase
- an apartment building during a fire

Writer's Word Bank
1. swarm
2. cradle
3. gallery
4. crimson
5. trapeze
6. festival

Planning

Choose an adventure to write about. *You* be the character telling the story. Use words like *I* and *my*. Set your story in a high-interest location. You may choose one of the settings in Sensational Story Settings. Or you may choose your own special setting. The choice is yours. Write a story that allows your readers to draw their own conclusions about something in the story. (You may use words from the Writer's Word Bank.) At the end of the story, write one question that the reader can answer by drawing conclusions.

CLUES TO USE

- Writers use story clues, facts, and details to help readers draw conclusions.
- Writers use clues to encourage readers to compare story events with their own experiences.

Plan your story on the lines below.

Main idea: _____

Setting: _____

Notes: _____

_____

_____

Question: _____

Writing

On the lines below, write your first-person adventure story. Don't forget to include the question at the end.

_____

_____

_____

_____

_____

_____

_____

_____

_____

_____

Editing

Check to see if you included enough clues to help your readers draw a correct conclusion about something in the story. Is the setting of the story interesting? Did you write a first-person story? If not, go back and make the necessary changes.

Sharing

You will read your first-person story and the ending question to the class. Your teacher will tell you when to share and discuss your story with your classmates. Ask your classmates to identify the clues in the story that helped them answer the question.

ON YOUR OWN

Choose a character from a favorite poem, story, or movie. Pretend that you are that character. You may be Jim Hawkins of *Treasure Island,* Laura Ingalls of *Little House on the Prairie,* Humpty Dumpty of nursery-rhyme fame, or any other character you wish to be. (Angela likes to pretend that she's Ursula from *The Little Mermaid.*) Write a journal entry detailing one event in your life and how you felt about it. Write your journal entry on a separate piece of paper. In My Word Bank, write four important words you will use in your entry.

My Word Bank
1. _____
2. _____
3. _____
4. _____

Your Good Judgment

Think Before You Leap

Readers draw conclusions based on information that the writer provides in a story or an article. Sometimes the information makes the writer's message very obvious and clear. Other times the information requires the reader to think carefully before drawing conclusions about what the writer is saying.

Read the story that follows. As you read, think about the details the writer includes to help readers draw some important conclusions.

Conclusions on a Rainy Day

The father and son were sitting outside the principal's office. A woman came into the room carrying a closed umbrella. She asked one of the office people a question, then quickly left.

"What did you notice about that woman?" the father asked his son.

"Nothing special," the boy answered.

"She's expecting rain," the father said. After a few moments, he continued, "I could tell that just from looking at her. Do you know why?"

"No," the boy answered quietly.

"Because she was carrying an umbrella and wearing a rainhat."

"Maybe it's already started to rain," the boy suggested.

"No, her rain gear is dry. Now, that's what you would call drawing a conclusion. When you draw conclusions, you not only consider what you see but also what you don't see."

What details, not seen by the son, helped the father draw conclusions? _____

_____

Now read another part of the story that takes place a little later.

Just then, a tall, thin man walked into the office, took off his wet raincoat, shook it over the wastebasket, hung it up, and sneezed loudly.

Now what conclusion could the father and son draw about the weather?

_____

As you write your next story, think about the many ways you can help readers draw conclusions to make their reading more interesting.

WRITER'S CORNER

Brainstorming
Telltale Clues

- COLD: mittens, heavy coats, boots, snow
- JOY: smiles, happy faces, laughter, party
- DANGER: warning signs, darkness, eerie sounds
- WELCOME: welcome mat, greetings, hugs, open arms

Writer's Word Bank
1. snowflake
2. squash
3. musician
4. mathematics
5. automobile
6. passageway

Planning

Write a story that has two characters. Have the two characters give clues to help readers draw conclusions about what is happening. Clues can be provided through the characters' conversation or actions. Provide an effective setting to feature your clues. You may choose an idea and details from Telltale Clues or use whatever idea and details you wish. (You may use words from the Writer's Word Bank.)

CLUES TO USE
• Write from your own experiences.
• Use clues that help readers figure out what is happening.

Plan your writing on the lines below.

Setting: _____

Readers will be able to draw the conclusion that_____

_____ .

Details that will help readers draw their conclusion: _____

_____

_____

Writing

On the lines below, write your short story about two characters. End with the question "What conclusions can you draw from the story?"

_____

_____

_____

_____

_____

_____

_____

_____

_____

_____

_____

_____

_____

_____

Editing

Check to see if you have provided enough clues to help your readers draw correct conclusions. Does your story involve two characters? Is the setting clear? Does the setting help the readers understand the story clues? If not, go back and make the necessary changes. (Every now and then Angela needs a change of setting to lift her spirits.)

Sharing

Find an appropriate picture from a magazine to illustrate your story. Mount the finished copy of your story and the illustration on large construction paper. Your teacher will tell you where to hang your product for other students to read.

ON YOUR OWN

Find a brief, interesting story in a newspaper or a magazine. Choose a story that is about people. Rewrite the story on a separate piece of paper. Replace the people in the story with people you know. Change the setting to one that is familiar. Add any new ideas that will improve your story. In My Word Bank, write four important words you will use in your story. Mount the newspaper or magazine story and your story side by side on a large piece of construction paper. Display your work so you and your classmates may compare stories.

My Word Bank
1. _____
2. _____
3. _____
4. _____

Building the Writer's Word Power

swarm
cradle
gallery
crimson
trapeze
festival

A. *If It's Not, It Might Be*

In the English language, two or more words may
express the same or nearly the same meaning.

Use what you know about the underlined words to help you complete the
sentences.

1. If it's not <u>red</u>, it might be _____ .

2. If it's not a <u>crib</u>, it might be a _____ .

3. If it's not a <u>celebration</u>, it might be a _____ .

4. If it's not a <u>bunch</u>, it might be a _____ .

5. If it's not a <u>swing</u>, it might be a _____ .

6. If it's not a <u>museum</u>, it might be a _____ .

B. *Picto-Words*

Picto-words can be fun for writers. Their meanings can be explained by how the letters of each word are drawn.

Choose one word from the box that is related to each picto-word. Write the related words on the lines. Then draw a picto-word for each.

| snowflake |
| squash |
| musician |
| mathematics |
| automobile |
| passageway |

Picto-Words	Related Words	Picto-Words
1. *Melody*	1. _____	1.
2. ARI+HME+IC	2. _____	2.
3. **raindrop**	3. _____	3.
4. STAIRWAY	4. _____	4.
5. T●MAT●	5. _____	5.
6. *BICYCLE*	6. _____	6.

What Makes Things Happen?

Never Touch a Frantic Gorilla

Writers depend on the readers' senses to make their stories seem true to life. Angela knows this. She will tell you that good writers are concerned with the sights, sounds, feelings, tastes, and smells that readers are able to imagine. For example, if the setting of a story is a kitchen, the writer might bring that setting to life by describing the smells of cooking that a character is experiencing. Read the following story part to see how the writer uses the senses, along with cause and effect, to create an interesting story.

Anna balanced the book straight up on her desk and continued to read. A breeze blew in from the open window against the balanced book. "Cause!" Anna said to herself. The book fell backward onto her desk. "Effect!" she mumbled, quite pleased with herself. She picked up the book, balanced it once again, and continued reading.

While reading, she only half heard a funny rumbling noise, like the sound of a distant subway train.

The rumbling grew louder, and Anna soon felt where the sound was coming from. She laughed.

"That's the effect!" she said, looking down at her noisy stomach.

Then she blew hard against the book, and it fell over one more time. And if the book had had a sense of smell, it would certainly have known that the cause of the noise was a pepperoni pizza!

What did Anna hear? _____

_____

What did Anna feel? _____

_____

What did Anna smell? _____

_____

The story makes good use of the readers' senses and has several examples of cause and effect. For example, if the effect was the rumbling of Anna's stomach, what was the cause? _____

_____

Write one other cause-and-effect example. _____

_____

Where's Angela?
Clue: Angela always has the time to figure out a perfect rhyme.

WRITER'S CORNER

Brainstorming
Touch, Taste, and Tambourines

- SIGHT: a frantic gorilla, a swimming lifeguard, a rain forest
- HEARING: scratching dogs, the blast of a horn, the thump and rattle of tambourines
- TOUCH: the roughness of sandpaper, the coldness of ice
- TASTE: sweet frosting, sour lemons, salted popcorn
- SMELL: tulips, a turkey roasting, polluted water

Writer's Word Bank
1. litter
2. pupil
3. column
4. issue
5. features
6. channel

Planning

Choose a city street, the stage of a theater, or the school cafeteria as a setting for a story. Complete the chart on page 48 by writing sense words and phrases you will use in your story. Perhaps you would like to use some ideas listed in Touch, Taste, and Tambourines. (You may use words from the Writer's Word Bank.)

CLUES TO USE
- Write clue words that appeal to the senses.
- Use cause and effect to write an interesting story.
- The cause is the reason something happens; the effect is what happens.

Plan your writing on the lines below. Then complete the chart.

Setting: _____

The problem: _____

The cause of the problem: _____

The effect of the problem: _____

Sense Chart

Sight	Hearing	Touch	Taste	Smell

Writing

On the lines below and on the next page, write your story. Include details that appeal to the senses. Use cause and effect. Tell your story in one or two paragraphs.

_____

_____

_____

_____

_____

_____

_____

_____

_____

_____

_____

_____

_____

Editing

Check to be sure that your story contains words and phrases that appeal to the senses. (Angela loves bubble bath, so she uses a lot of "smelly" words.) Did you create an interesting problem? Are the cause and effect clear? If your answer is *No* to either question, go back and improve your story.

Sharing

Write your final copy on a separate piece of paper. Give your story a catchy title. Your teacher will tell you when to share your story with your classmates. After you read the story, ask the listeners to identify the problem, as well as its cause and effect.

---

*O*N YOUR OWN

Plan a one-page or two-page school newspaper, alone or with a friend. On separate paper, write several articles that will interest your classmates. Remember to include WHO, WHAT, WHEN, WHERE, and WHY when writing the news articles. Create a headline for each article. Your school newspaper should be like a real newspaper. You may wish to include some ads and a cartoon. In My Word Bank, write four important words you will use in your articles. (If you need help thinking of ideas to write about, check the Topic Ideas on page 106.) Put your finished newspaper on the class bulletin board.

My Word Bank
1. _____
2. _____
3. _____
4. _____

What Makes Things Happen?

A Point of View

Often, stories or articles present a particular point of view. For example, a writer who favors the use of natural gas as an energy source would write an article on the subject from that point of view, while a writer who favors fossil fuel would write a very different article. (Did you know that Angela believes natural gas is the cause of hiccups?)

A point of view tells how an author (sometimes through his or her characters) feels about an issue. Read the story that follows. The story is about pollution and is told from a sea gull's point of view. As you read, look for two examples of cause and effect.

Today is a day like any other for Nancy Sea Gull. After breakfast, she will fly up and down the coast, searching for signs of oil spills. Ever since a tanker was grounded off the coast of Maine two years ago, Nancy has taken it upon herself to fight those who pollute the ocean. After her pollution patrol, it will be lunchtime. As always, Nancy will have lunch near one of the local hospitals. That way she can entertain the patients when she's through eating.

CAUSE AND EFFECT

Did you notice that the author treats the sea gull like a person? The author provides the sea gull with humanlike qualities. This writing technique is called *personification*. Personification can add much interest to a story.

Now consider how the author uses cause and effect.

Because of the oil spill, Nancy _____

_____.

Because Nancy likes to entertain the patients, she _____

_____.

The author combines personification and cause and effect to increase the interest. In addition, the author chooses to tell the story from the point of view of the sea gull. Part of the joy of writing is the mixing of techniques. The author of Nancy Sea Gull has done this well.

WRITER'S CORNER

Brainstorming
Conflicting Points of View

- dieter: broiled foods or fried foods
- vacationer: the mountains or the seashore
- coach: most able player or most popular player
- car buyer: large car or small car

Writer's Word Bank
1. snare
2. rhyme
3. stool
4. prime
5. mound
6. lumber

Planning

Choose a topic for a story or an article. Let the topic be one that you have strong feelings about. Use one or two examples of cause and effect to emphasize your point of view. Perhaps you would like to include ideas suggested by Conflicting Points of View. The choice is yours. You may also wish to use personification to add interest to your story. (You may use words from the Writer's Word Bank.)

CLUES TO USE
- Writers often tell a story from a particular point of view.
- Writers use cause and effect to create interesting stories.
- Personification provides animals and objects with humanlike qualities.

Plan your point-of-view writing on the lines below. Use cause and effect.

Topic: _____

Notes: _____

_____

_____

_____

_____

_____

_____

Writing

On the lines below and on the next page, write your point-of-view story or article in two or three paragraphs. (As you would expect, Angela has a point of view about everything.)

_____

_____

_____

_____

_____

_____

_____

_____

_____

_____

_____

_____

_____

_____

_____

_____

_____

_____

Editing

Check to be sure that you used cause and effect in your story. Is your point of view clear? Did you leave out important details? If you did, go back and make changes.

Sharing

Write your final copy on a separate piece of paper. Give your story a catchy title. Find or draw an illustration to complete your story. Your teacher will tell you when to share your story and illustration with your classmates.

*O*N YOUR OWN

Here's a point-of-view activity that should be fun to write. Choose a child's story like "The Three Little Pigs" or "Snow White." Though the story you choose will have already been rewritten many times by many authors, you will write it again. But your story will have a different point of view. For example, you could write "The Three Little Pigs" from the wolf's point of view, or "Snow White" from the evil queen's point of view. In My Word Bank, write four important words you will use in your writing. On separate paper, develop your own book with Ilustrations. Read and share your finished book with a younger writer.

My Word Bank

1. _____

2. _____

3. _____

4. _____

Building the Writer's Word Power

litter
pupil
column
issue
features
channel

A. *Two in One*

Word meaning is important to writers. When using a word with more than one meaning, careful writers make sure that the correct meaning is clear.

Choose one word from the box that can be written twice to complete each sentence.

1. The magazine article _____ local tourist attractions

   and their many exciting _____ .

2. The captain will _____ the barge into a wider

   _____ .

3. A _____ in our class injured the

   _____ of her eye.

4. A _____ of puppies can quickly

   _____ an area.

5. The publisher will _____ a second _____ of
   the newsletter.

6. "A _____ of troops stood guard," she reported in

   her weekly news _____ .

B. *Matched Pairs*

Rhyming words can make writing more pleasurable and entertaining.

Read each sentence clue. Then pair a word from the box with a familiar rhyming word. Write the word pair that completes each sentence.

snare
rhyme
stool
prime
mound
lumber

Sample: Halloween might be called <u>fright</u> <u>night</u>.

1. Many evening television programs are on _____

   _____ .

2. You might catch an old grizzly with a _____

   _____ .

3. Someone who counts logs would know the _____

   _____ .

4. A classroom seat might be called a _____

   _____ .

5. A slight bump in the earth may be a _____

   _____ .

6. A poem about a robbery would be a _____

   _____ .

VOCABULARY AND SPELLING

Between the Lines

Angela is quick to tell anyone who will listen that reading is a guessing game. When she says this, listeners usually look at her strangely. However, after they think about what she is saying, they often change their expressions. Angela will tell you that when you read, you read the printed *lines* and you also read what is "between the lines." Reading is the combining of what is said with what is *inferred*. Readers use both kinds of information to make accurate guesses about what is going on in a story.

Read the letter that follows. See what information you can *infer* by reading "between the lines."

Dear John,

I waited three days for you, but you never showed up at the ski lodge. Finally, having no more money, I had to check out of the lodge. This is the fifth time you have let me down. I know we have a good time when we ski together, but I have better things to do than wait around for you. I am not angry, but I do think you owe me an explanation.

Your cousin,
Martin

In the letter, does Martin say he is angry? _____

Is he really angry? _____

What words in the letter lead you to think he's probably angry? _____

_____

You have to figure out that Martin is angry, even though he writes that he isn't. This kind of figuring out is called *inferring.* To reach the answer, you have to go beyond the written words and think about what the writer is letting you know without saying directly.

Where's Angela?
Clue: *A fall from here is quite a drop; she's hiding near a mountaintop.*

WRITER'S CORNER

Brainstorming
Cool Comic Characters

- Batman corners Joker in "card" shop.
- Dick Tracy transmits secret message.
- Donald Duck drives Daisy daffy.
- Lone Ranger loses Silver.

Writer's Word Bank

1. furious
2. incredible
3. extinct
4. cruel
5. unexpected
6. stern

Planning

Cut out a favorite comic strip from the Sunday newspaper comic section. Notice the "bubbles" that contain words the characters say. Glue strips of white paper over the bubbles so that all "spoken" words are covered. Plan a new story to tell. You will use the same pictures, but you will write your own words for the characters to say. (You may use words from the Writer's Word Bank.)

CLUES TO USE
- Writers sometimes give clues that help readers infer what is going on.
- Writers sometimes give clues to help readers infer what is happening from what the characters say to each other.

INFERRING

Plan the story and the words the characters will say in the comic strip.

Notes: _____

_____

_____

_____

_____

_____

_____

Writing

In the speech bubbles, write the words each character will say to tell the story. Use the words of the speaker or speakers to help readers infer what is happening in the comic strip.

Editing

Check to be sure that readers can infer what is happening in the story from what the characters are saying. If any part of the story is not clear, go back and rewrite that part more clearly.

Sharing

The finished comic strips can be put on the class bulletin board for your classmates to read and enjoy. Later, the strips can be assembled into a book and placed in the class library.

My Word Bank

1. _____

2. _____

3. _____

4. _____

Imagine that you are a cartoonist who's been hired to develop a new comic strip. You may work alone or with a partner. Create your own characters and story line. Plan your story on the lines below. Then, on a piece of art paper, draw your characters in six or more story frames.

Plan what the characters will say in each frame, and write the characters' words in special bubbles. In My Word Bank, write four important words you will use in your comic strip. (If you need help thinking of an idea to write about, check the Topic Ideas on page 106.)

_____

_____

_____

_____

_____

_____

_____

_____

_____

_____

_____

_____

_____

_____

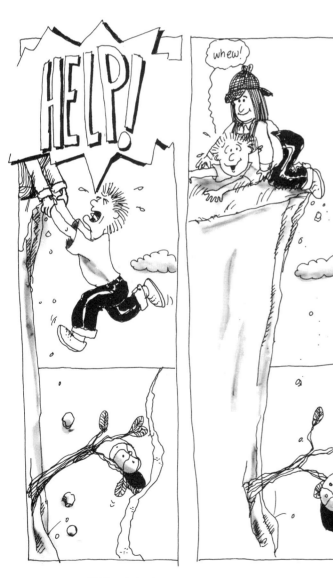

No Surprises!

Good writers know the importance of careful planning. Some writers use brainstorming maps similar to the one below to plan their stories. (Angela always draws up a plan before she starts to write.)

The Surprise

I awoke to a familiar sound—the banging of pots and pans.

My two children planned a surprise for my special day.

Eggshells and flour were scattered everywhere.

I went downstairs and peeked into the kitchen.

One year ago they had surprised me in the same way.

Pots, pans, and dishes were everywhere.

Perhaps they were surprising me again.

Read the two paragraphs that were developed from the brainstorming map on page 60. As you read, notice how the author helps the reader infer that the children are preparing a birthday surprise.

The Surprise

I was very suspicious when I awoke to the sound of clanging pots and pans from downstairs. The last time I heard that sound was one year ago today. On that day my children had surprised me by waking up early in the morning, making a mess downstairs, and then coming upstairs as if nothing had happened. Usually I get very angry when someone upsets my pots, pans, and dishes. However, the look on their faces had told me to keep quiet.

Were they going to surprise me again this year? I decided to go downstairs and sneak a peek. I opened the kitchen door about two inches. Eggshells were scattered on the floor and on the table. Both of my children were covered from head to toe with a layer of white powder, one of the ingredients required for the special meal they were fixing.

Note how closely the writer follows the brainstorming map. What was the birthday surprise the children were fixing? _____

_____

What makes you think so? _____

_____

WRITER'S CORNER

Brainstorming
Wishbones and Wishing Stones

- Maria's report card is stolen by a sea gull.
- Brandon's friend plants a potato pie.
- Carla's dog climbs a tree.
- Lenny's car is attacked by a moose.
- Madeline's pet knits sleeveless sweaters.

Writer's Word Bank
1. multiply
2. hurricane
3. scowl
4. ostrich
5. cabbage
6. launch

Planning

Choose an unusual event to write a story about. The event should be a problem for the main character in your story. You may choose an event suggested in Wishbones and Wishing Stones, or you may come up with an idea of your own. Develop a brainstorming map to plan your story. Write the main idea in the center of the map. Let the details grow out of the main idea. (You may use words from the Writer's Word Bank.)

CLUES TO USE
- Write clues that help readers infer what is going on.
- Write clues that help readers infer what is happening from what the characters say to each other.

Develop the brainstorming map of your story.

Title: _____

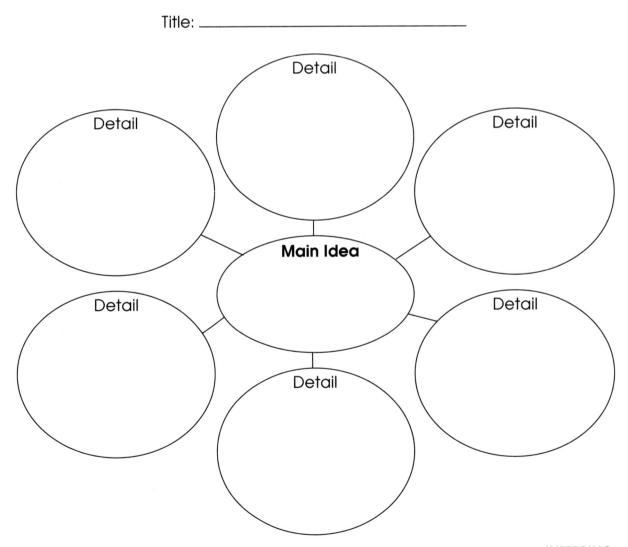

INFERRING

Writing

On the lines below, write the story that follows the plan you developed in your brainstorming map. If you need more space, write your story on a separate piece of paper.

_____

_____

_____

_____

_____

_____

_____

Editing

Check to be sure that your story provides clues that let readers infer what is happening. Did you present enough clues? If not, go back and add some clues. Change any clues that are not clear.

Sharing

Your teacher will tell you when to share your map and your story with your classmates.

ON YOUR OWN

A Big Book is a very large book with pictures and oversized print. Create a Big Book for your classmates or for younger children. Use a brainstorming map to plan your story. Your story should be no longer than eight pages. Use art paper for the pages. Write a few lines on each page and draw an illustration that goes with that part of the story. On the last page, write two questions. Each question should ask the readers to infer something from the clues given in the story. In My Word Bank, write four important words you will use in your story. Put your finished book in the class library. (If you need help thinking of an idea to write about, check the Topic Ideas on page 106.)

My Word Bank

1. _____

2. _____

3. _____

4. _____

Building the Writer's Word Power

furious
incredible
extinct
cruel
unexpected
stern

A. *Better Choices*

Writers are always making word choices. They work hard to choose words that make their stories clear.

Read each sentence. Choose a word from the box to improve the underlined phrase in each sentence.

Sentences   **Better Choices**

1. The height of the skyscraper was <u>not to be believed</u>.

   _____

2. The arrival of cold weather was <u>something we had not planned for</u>.

   _____

3. I was assigned to a <u>firm and strict</u> teacher.

   _____

4. The manager was <u>filled with extreme anger</u>.

   _____

5. Why is the enemy so <u>willing to cause pain and suffering</u>?

   _____

6. The mammoth elephant <u>is no longer in existence</u>.

   _____

| multiply |
| hurricane |
| scowl |
| ostrich |
| cabbage |
| launch |

B. *Group Connections*

Sometimes writers group words into categories.

Choose a word from the box to add to each category.

1. A tornado, a blizzard, and a _____ are kinds of storms.

2. Lettuce, spinach, and _____ are leafy vegetables.

3. A jay, an eagle, and an _____ are kinds of birds.

4. A freighter, a liner, and a _____ are kinds of watercraft.

5. A smile, a frown, and a _____ are facial expressions.

6. *Add, divide,* and _____ are arithmetic terms.

VOCABULARY AND SPELLING

Something to Choose

It's Your Decision

Good writers know that good stories depend upon interesting characters. One of the ways writers make their characters interesting is by providing them with decisions to make. Readers can readily relate to characters who make decisions because readers have to make decisions every day of their lives. (On school mornings, Angela spends a lot of time deciding what she will eat for breakfast. Her choice is always the same —raisin cereal and orange juice. Angela is in a rut; she needs to add variety to her decisions.)

Read the article about Eskimos and seals. Note how both Eskimos and seals must make decisions in order to survive.

A Matter of Life or Death

It is very cold in the northern areas of Alaska where Eskimos live— too cold to grow vegetables or raise animals. So, some Eskimos hunt for their food. The seal is the main animal hunted by Eskimos living near the shore. Since there are few kinds of animals available to them, the Eskimos must be good at hunting seals if they want to stay alive.

Hunting for seals is a tricky matter. Seals, like people, need to breathe air. Even though they live in the water, they must come up for a breath of air now and then. An Eskimo hunter searches for a hole in the ice and then waits for a seal to come along. All of this works pretty well unless the seal is already near the hole.

If the seal is near the hole, it can hear the Eskimo walking up to the hole. If it doesn't hear footsteps leaving the hole, the seal knows that there is more than air waiting at the hole. A smart seal will say "No, thanks!" and swim off to find another hole.

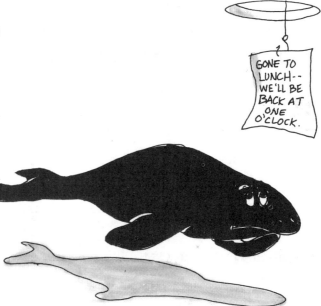

Can you figure out what the Eskimo hunters do in order to fool the seals? Here's a hint: It takes two Eskimos to trick a seal into thinking that an air hole is safe.

MAKING DECISIONS

Write one decision the Eskimo hunter must make. _____

_____

Write one decision the seal must make. _____

_____

How do Eskimo hunters fool the seals? _____

_____

Where's Angela?
Clue: Angela eats only lean meat; find her near a tasty treat.

WRITER'S CORNER

Brainstorming
Split Decisions

- Quarterback—Should I run with the football or attempt a pass?
- Baby-sitter—Should I put the children to bed or let them stay up longer?
- Police officer—Should I warn the speeder or give the speeder a ticket?
- Physician—Should I operate on the patient or continue to treat the patient with medicine?

Writer's Word Bank
1. scent
2. governor
3. astonish
4. proceed
5. argue
6. amateur

Planning

Think of a character who has a tough decision to make. The character may be real or imaginary and could even be you or one of your friends or relatives. You may even choose one of the characters listed in Split Decisions. Plan a short story that features your character and involves two choices that present a decision-making problem for the character. (You may use words from the Writer's Word Bank.)

CLUES TO USE
- Writers include information to help readers understand why characters make the choices they do.
- Writers consider how readers will react to the choices their characters make.

Plan your writing on the lines and on the charts.

My character: _____

Choice 1: _____

Choice 2: _____

CHOICE 1	
Reasons FOR	**Reasons AGAINST**
_____	_____
_____	_____
_____	_____
_____	_____
_____	_____
_____	_____

CHOICE 2	
Reasons FOR	**Reasons AGAINST**
_____	_____
_____	_____
_____	_____
_____	_____
_____	_____
_____	_____

Solution: _____

MAKING DECISIONS

Writing

On the lines below, write your short story about a character who makes a tough decision. If you need more space, write your story on a separate piece of paper.

_____

_____

_____

_____

_____

_____

Editing

Check to be sure that your character's two choices are clearly explained. Did you provide the reason for the final decision? Did you leave out important details? If you did, go back and make changes.

Sharing

Your teacher will tell you when to share your writing orally with your classmates. First, introduce your character. Next, explain the two choices that your character faces. Also explain the reasons for and against each choice. Then ask your classmates to predict which choice the character will make and to explain why they made this prediction. Finally, read your story.

*O*N YOUR OWN

Choose one historical character who had a difficult decision to make. For example, in 1795 Alexander Hamilton agreed to fight a duel with Aaron Burr. Research your character in the library. On a separate piece of paper, write a brief biography of your character, including an account of the difficult decision and its effect on his or her life. Do not reveal your character's name. Read your biography to your classmates

My Word Bank
1. _____
2. _____
3. _____
4. _____

and see if they can guess who your character is. In My Word Bank, write four important words you will use in your biography. (If you need help thinking of a historical character to write about, check your social studies book.)

Truth or Consequences

In school, every student gets accustomed to reading articles. For example, when you study about explorers in America, you read the articles in your social studies book about the explorers. Most textbook writers work hard to make the articles interesting. They write the information in ways that will help students remember the facts. Students must make decisions about which facts are important. Students must remember the important facts in order to prepare themselves for answering questions at the end of a chapter.

Read the article about farming. Be ready to make decisions about the answer to the question that follows.

The Discovery of Farming: An Idea That Changed the World*

No one knows for sure how farming first began. Like many great discoveries, it probably happened by accident. Someone may have dropped some seeds of wild wheat on the ground one fall. The next spring that person may have found a crop growing in the spot where he or she dropped the seeds.

No matter how it came about, we do know that sometime between 10,000 B.C. and 8,000 B.C. people began to grow crops and raise animals.

Early farmers used sticks with sharp ends to break up the ground for planting. These digging sticks led to the hoe. The first hoe was probably a forked stick. Farmers would pull this forked stick toward them to stir up the ground. And this hoe led to the plow.

When readers answer multiple-choice questions, they have to make decisions. Which answer is the best choice?

What does the invention of the plow tell you?

   a. Early farmers were clever inventors.

   b. Inventions often grow out of other inventions.

   c. Most early inventions were made of wood.

The writer of the article provides information to support the second answer as the best choice.

*From *What's to Eat?*, the 1979 Yearbook of the United States Department of Agriculture.

WRITER'S CORNER

Brainstorming
State Just the Facts

- The earliest wheelbarrow was designed around 200 A.D. by Chunko Liang, a general in the Chinese army.
- The first sandwich was created by John Montague, earl of Sandwich, in 1762.
- Josephine Cochrane designed the first dishwasher in Illinois, sometime around 1880.

Planning

The persons in State Just the Facts had decisions to make, and the decisions they made led to inventions. Think of a person who has had a decision to make. Your choice may be an explorer, an inventor, a great leader, or anyone else you wish. Plan a short journal entry about the decision this person made. Write the entry as if it were written by the person. Then let your readers do some decision making by presenting them with one multiple-choice question about the information in the journal entry. Provide three or four answer choices, but be sure that only one choice is correct. (You may use words from the Writer's Word Bank.)

CLUES TO USE

- Writers include important facts that help readers understand why people make the decisions they do.
- Writers of articles help readers make decisions about what information is the most important to remember.

MAKING DECISIONS

Plan your writing on the lines below.

The person: _____

Notes: _____

_____

_____

_____

_____

Writing

On the lines below, write the journal entry that your chosen person might have written.

_____

_____

_____

_____

_____

_____

_____

_____

_____

_____

_____

Multiple-choice question: _____

_____

_____

Editing

Check to be sure that your journal entry focuses on a decision that the person had to make. Did you write facts to help readers understand why the person made a particular choice? If not, go back and make the changes.

Sharing

Your teacher will tell you when to share your journal entry with your classmates.

ON YOUR OWN

Many people keep journals. Travelers, scientists, and writers are just a few of the people who often use journals to record the events in their lives. Keep a journal of the events that happen to you each day for two weeks. You can make a journal by stapling eight pages of lined paper together. Write at least one paragraph each day. Include the date each time you make an entry. Record any difficult decisions you had to make and the facts that helped you decide as you did. (Angela has kept a diary for years. She often tells her brother that her diary is her own private journal. For him, the diary is off limits!) In My Word Bank, write four important words you will use in your journal.

My Word Bank

1. _____

2. _____

3. _____

4. _____

Something to Choose

Building the Writer's Word Power

scent
governor
astonish
proceed
argue
amateur

A. *A Question of Substitutes*

Writers often use synonyms to vary their writing. Substitute a synonym from the box for each underlined word or phrase.

1. Should we <u>move on</u> to the next step? _____

2. When did the leaders <u>quarrel</u>? _____

3. Why does the <u>smell</u> of perfume fill the room? _____

4. How many players are <u>not professional</u> athletes? _____

5. Who is the <u>chief officer</u> of your state? _____

6. Did the magician <u>fill</u> you <u>with wonder</u>? _____

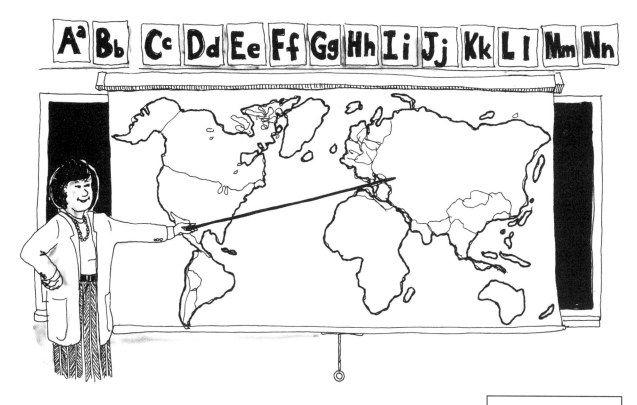

B. *The Numbers Game*

Writers sometimes use number clues to provide readers with information.

Read each number clue. Then write the word from the box that fits the clue.

century
lobster
continent
clover
meter
temperature

1. one of seven great landmasses _____

2. four leaves on a lucky one _____

3. ten times ten years _____

4. a healthy one at ninety-eight point six degrees

    _____

5. a little more than thirty-nine inches _____

6. gets around with four pairs of small legs and one pair of claws

    _____

Mind Talk

Good writers sometimes use fantasy to tell their stories. Writers of fairy tales, folktales, fables, and legends have been using fantasy effectively for hundreds of years. Fantasy writers use unreal situations to express real thoughts and feelings. It's usually easy to tell the difference between fantasy and reality. If you have difficulty knowing the difference, just ask yourself if the events in the story could possibly happen. (Angela kissed a frog once, but no prince appeared. So much for Angela's fantasy.)

Read the story about Roberta. As you read, ask yourself if Roberta's "conscience" is an example of reality or fantasy.

Roberta edged over to the reading table at the back of the classroom. She picked up her book and returned quietly to her desk. She opened the book to the lesson and read "What Is Real?"

"You're supposed to be doing your math work now," said a quiet voice behind her. Roberta turned, even though she had recognized the voice. It was Roberta's conscience.

"Don't bother me," said Roberta. "I want to read another lesson—just one more, that's all. After that I'll do my math."

Roberta's conscience laughed. "That's what you said yesterday. And you ended up with no recess. It's always 'just one more.' When will you ever learn?"

How does the writer use fantasy to explore Roberta's guilty feelings?

_____

Angela often relies on her conscience to keep herself out of trouble. However, Angela's conscience is not a person. Her conscience is her thoughts. Angela often uses thoughts to help her make the right choices. What do you use?

Where's Angela?
Clue: They say that Angela now has met
a friendly girl who's named Annette.

WRITER'S CORNER

Brainstorming
Folk Heroes and Legends

- The Erie Canal—a canal-boat mule driver named McCarthy became the legendary strongman of the canal in the 1840s.
- The Mississippi River—Mike Fink was a legendary keel-boatman and a most daring wild-forest hunter of the 1840s.
- The Northwest—Sacajawea became a legend after she led Lewis and Clark across dangerous wilderness territory to the Pacific Ocean in the early 1800s.

Writer's Word Bank
1. auditorium
2. nursery
3. supermarket
4. academy
5. dungeon
6. lodge

Planning

Write a newspaper article about a not-so-famous folk hero. Tell WHO the hero is, WHAT the hero did, WHEN and WHERE the hero did it, and WHY. You may write about a folk hero listed in Folk Heroes and Legends or any other folk hero of your choice. When reporting about your hero, write information that will help make your hero a legend. Write a catchy headline for your article. You may need to use the school library to find information about your hero. (You may use words from the Writer's Word Bank.)

Plan your newspaper article on the lines below.

WHO: _____

_____

WHAT: _____

_____

WHEN: _____

_____

WHERE: _____

_____

WHY: _____

_____

HEADLINE: _____

Writing

On the lines below and on the next page, write a newspaper article about a folk hero. Include a catchy headline to introduce your article.

_____

_____

_____

_____

_____

_____

FANTASY OR REALITY

_____

_____

_____

_____

_____

_____

_____

_____

Editing

Check to be sure that your folk hero article includes the five *W*'s: WHO, WHAT, WHEN, WHERE, and WHY. Did you include a catchy headline? Did you write information that will help make your folk hero a legend? Go back and make any necessary changes.

Sharing

Your teacher will tell you when to share your folk article with your classmates. You will present your hero orally to the class. If you can, dress up as your folk hero to make your presentation more interesting.

ON YOUR OWN

There are many women and men living today who will become tomorrow's folk heroes. Write a two-character television interview involving one such woman or man. You may work alone or with a partner. Let one character be the interviewer and the second character be the future folk hero. Have the interviewer ask questions about the folk hero's life and accomplishments, and have the folk hero respond with answers that are based on fact but that greatly exaggerate the truth. Plan your interview on separate paper. In My Word Bank, write four important words you will use in your writing. You may be asked to stage your interview for your classmates. (If you need help thinking of an idea to write about, check the Topic Ideas on page 106.)

> **My Word Bank**
>
> 1. _____
>
> 2. _____
>
> 3. _____
>
> 4. _____

Stretching the Truth

The Real and the Unreal

Have you ever read a story about a fierce battle in a strange world between a lone sword-swinging warrior and a towering tyrannosaurus? An exciting story perhaps, but it could happen only in a land of make-believe. The reality is that the last dinosaur died more than one hundred million years before the first human being walked on earth. Writers often mix fantasy and reality to create interesting stories and poems.

Read the poem about Annette. As you read, notice the realistic things that happen and the fantastic things that could never really happen.

Yes! Yes! Annette

1. Annette put on her roller skates
   And soared on down the street.
   She rolled along so very fast
   The ground never touched her feet.

2. Annette came down with hunger pains
   And said, "It's time for dinner.
   A cow is such a treat to eat.
   It's sure to make me thinner!"

3. Annette grew tired and took a nap
   Beneath a thick green hedge.
   She never knew she slumbered near
   A narrow mountain ledge.

4. Annette snored and shook the clouds
   And caused the rain to shower.
   The storm awoke her and she gasped,
   "How did I get such power?"

FANTASY OR REALITY

Did you enjoy the poem? _____ Why or why not? _____

_____

What is the rhyming pattern of the poem? _____

_____

Write two real events from the poem. _____

_____

Write two examples of fantasy. _____

_____

WRITER'S CORNER

Brainstorming

Flights of Fancy

- The Scarlet Zebra from Zanzibar
- An Elephant's Trunk of Toys
- Giant Mice and Cats of Ice
- Mutants from the Ocean Depths
- Steel Gloves and Turtledoves

Writer's Word Bank
1. conduct
2. collect
3. mourn
4. inspect
5. entertain
6. stitch

Planning

Brainstorm topics that you could use to write an eight-line poem mixing reality and fantasy. Work to make your poem amusing. Select one of your own topics or borrow one from Flights of Fancy. Decide the rhyming pattern for your poem. (You may use words from the Writer's Word Bank.)

CLUES TO USE
- Writers sometimes mix fantasy with reality to create interesting stories and poems.
- Poets often use rhythm and rhyme to tell their stories in verse.

Plan your poem on the brainstorming map below.

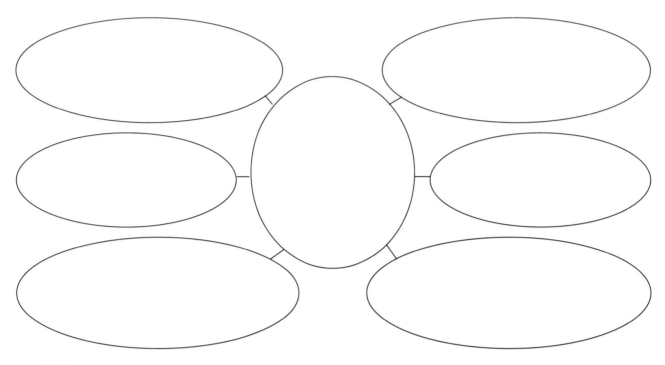

Writing

On the lines below, write your eight-line poem that combines fantasy with reality.

_____

_____

_____

_____

_____

_____

_____

_____

_____

_____

_____

Editing

Read your finished poem silently. Did you mix real events with fantasy? Did you use a rhyming pattern? If not, go back and make the necessary changes. (Angela believes that a poem is amusing if it makes her giggle. Will your poem make Angela giggle? How about a mild chuckle?)

Sharing

Your teacher will tell you when to share your poem. At that time, you and your classmates will sit in a circle with your completed poems mounted on art paper. Each person, in turn, will read his or her poem. As you listen to your classmates read, think of something positive to say about each poem.

ON YOUR OWN

A tercet is a poem that consists of three rhyming lines. Angela wrote the following tercet:

When she saw the hungry cat,
The tiny mouse scurried under the hat
And pulled away the welcome mat.

On the lines below, write two or three tercets that stretch the truth. Choose any topic. Then write your tercets on art paper and illustrate them. In My Word Bank, write four important words you will use in your poems. (If you need help thinking of an idea to write about, check the Topic Ideas on page 106.)

My Word Bank
1. _____
2. _____
3. _____
4. _____

_____

_____

_____

_____

_____

_____

_____

Stretching the Truth

Building the Writer's Word Power

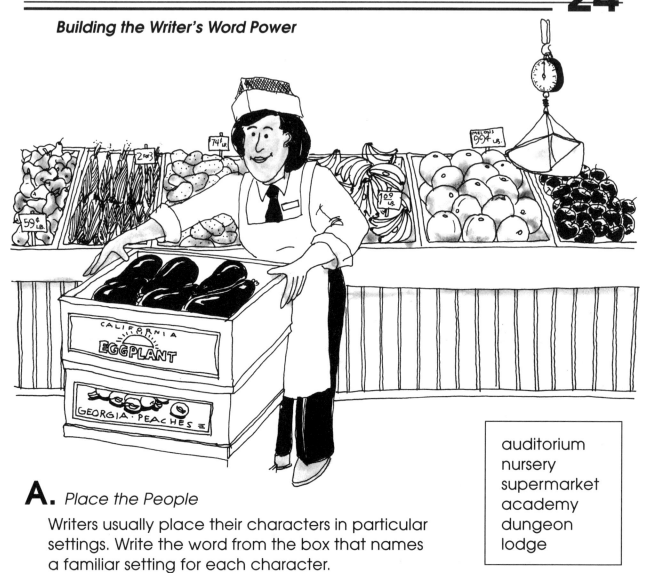

auditorium
nursery
supermarket
academy
dungeon
lodge

A. Place the People

Writers usually place their characters in particular settings. Write the word from the box that names a familiar setting for each character.

1. A writer might place a baby in the _____ .

2. A writer might place a speaker in the _____ .

3. A writer might place a prisoner in the _____ .

4. A writer might place a hunter in the _____ .

5. A writer might place a grocer in the _____ .

6. A writer might place a student in the _____ .

VOCABULARY AND SPELLING

B. *CharactERS and CreatORS*

Add *er* or *or* to words from the box to create some story characters. Write each character on the line provided.

1. This *or* character trades stamps or coins. _____

2. This *er* character has suffered a great loss. _____

3. This *or* character works on a train. _____

4. This *er* character sews clothing. _____

5. This *or* character investigates crime. _____

6. This *er* character sings and dances. _____

VOCABULARY AND SPELLING

A Convincing Argument

Who's Pushing Your Button?

"Who's pushing your button?" is a clever way of asking who is getting you to act and think the way you do. Consider Angela. She eats cherries because she read somewhere that cherries give people a healthy complexion. She is also saving her allowance to buy an expensive ZOOM bicycle, because she heard somewhere that everyone who knows anything about bicycles owns a ZOOM.

What do you think influenced Angela's decisions? Maybe the answer is advertising, which is part of a bigger idea—propaganda. Every day we see and hear advertisements—on TV, on the radio, in magazines, on posters, on billboards, and in newspapers. When a company wants you to buy its product, it often uses advertising to persuade you. Read the following advertisement. Think about the ways that the ad is trying to convince readers to buy new sneakers.

HURRY Limited Supply!

SPECIAL PRICE
$12.95

The first 1,000 orders will receive an autographed photo of MVP Kango Gazella, absolutely free!

Buy our new and better basketball shoes NOW and improve your game! HERCULES HOOVES will allow you to jump higher! HERCULES HOOVES are lightweight, slide-proof, and designed for faster starts and quicker stops!

Sizes 2–18   Colors: blue, gold, peppermint striped

Kango says . . .

"Ever since I donned

HERCULES HOOVES,

I've scored 6 more points per game."

Write two examples of propaganda that appear in the advertisement.

1. _____

2. _____

Where's Angela?
Clue: Look for Angela and you will note she's near
someone who'll win her vote.

WRITER'S CORNER

Brainstorming
Friendly Persuasion

- Caress Shampoo for luxurious hair
- Speedy Skateboards for the ride of a lifetime
- Forever Glue-Goo to mend a world of broken parts
- Fergie's Ice Cream, the king of desserts

Writer's Word Bank
1. spaghetti
2. raspberry
3. symphony
4. permanent
5. horror
6. chorus

Planning

Plan an advertisement that uses propaganda to influence readers. You may use an ad idea that appears in Friendly Persuasion or another idea. The choice is yours. Set up your final copy as a colorful ad with various sizes of print and an eye-catching illustration. Before you begin, you may wish to study the layout of ads that appear in current magazines. (You may use words from the Writer's Word Bank.)

CLUES TO USE
- Writers use propaganda to convince readers to agree with them.
- Propaganda often represents only one side of an issue.
- Advertisers use propaganda to get people to purchase a product.

Plan your writing on the lines below.

Product: _____

Key statements (including propaganda): _____

_____

_____

_____

_____

Writing

Write, design, and illustrate your advertisement in the box below.

PROPAGANDA

Editing

Check your advertisement to be sure that the propaganda you used isn't unbelievable. (Even when advertisers stretch the truth, their claims must be convincing.) Do the illustration and the statements work well together? If not, go back and make the necessary changes.

Sharing

Transfer the completed ad copy to art paper. Use color, design, and various sizes of print to get the most out of your ad. Place your finished ad on the bulletin board for others to read.

ON YOUR OWN

Imagine that you are the campaign manager for a candidate for public office. Your candidate may be a real or a fictional person. On a separate piece of paper, design a brief flyer or mailing piece about your candidate to send to the voters. The flyer should contain information that will convince the voters to support your candidate. Make the flyer colorful and eye-catching. Finished flyers can be displayed on the classroom walls. In My Word Bank, write four important words you will use in your writing.

My Word Bank

1. _____

2. _____

3. _____

4. _____

A Convincing Argument

Critic's Choice

A critic is a person who makes judgments about the strengths and weaknesses of something. An art critic makes judgments about the merits of paintings and other works of art. A drama critic makes judgments about the merits of stage productions. And movie critics make judgments about the merits of particular movies. Some critics are very convincing. Their judgments actually influence people's opinions of art, books, plays, and movies.

The following movie review was written for the radio. As you read the review, think of ways in which the announcer tries to convince listeners to see the movie.

Superfilms, Inc.

SUBJECT: *Angels from Mars*

MEDIUM: A thirty-second radio spot

ANNOUNCER: I want to tell you about a great space movie—one of the greatest movies ever made. The film is called *Angels from Mars*. If you liked *To Venus and Back*, *The Stars Are My Junkyard*, and *Star Bores*, you'll love *Angels from Mars*! Rip Connors stars as Holy Molar. It's his best role since *Second-Base Spaceman*. *Angels from Mars* is playing at the Little Run Theater. Hurry down as soon as you can. When people start to hear about this film, you will surely have to wait in a long line to see it.

The announcer uses propaganda to convince listeners to rush down to the Little Run Theater. Write two examples from the review.

1.＿＿＿＿＿＿＿＿＿＿＿＿＿＿＿＿＿＿＿＿＿＿＿＿＿＿＿＿＿＿＿＿＿＿

2.＿＿＿＿＿＿＿＿＿＿＿＿＿＿＿＿＿＿＿＿＿＿＿＿＿＿＿＿＿＿＿＿＿＿

Writers use many means to influence readers. The announcer who reviewed *Angel from Mars* used propaganda ("one of the greatest movies ever made"). The announcer also compared the new movie to other movies ("If you liked *To Venus and Back,* . . . you'll love *Angel from Mars!*"). Finally, the announcer suggested that the movie will be a big hit (". . . you will surely have to wait in a long line to see it").

Writer's Corner

Brainstorming
Picky! Picky! Picky!
Review the strengths and weaknesses of
- a school event such as an art fair or concert
- a special celebration
- a new singing group
- a football game between rival schools

Writer's Word Bank
1. fringe
2. spare
3. siren
4. crate
5. cheap
6. alert

Planning

Plan a review of an event or a performance. Choose an idea from Picky! Picky! Picky! or choose an idea of your own. Emphasize either the strengths or the weaknesses of the event. Use propaganda to influence readers to agree with you. (You may use words from the Writer's Word Bank.)

PROPAGANDA

Plan your writing on the lines below, listing both strengths and weaknesses.

Event: _____

STRENGTHS	WEAKNESSES
_____	_____
_____	_____
_____	_____
_____	_____
_____	_____

Writing

On the lines below and on the next page, write your review about an event or a performance. Choose either to praise or to "pan" the event. Emphasize the strengths or the weaknesses. Be convincing.

_____

_____

_____

_____

_____

_____

_____

_____

_____

_____

_____

_____

_____

Editing

Check to be sure that your review emphasizes the merits or the faults of the event. Is your writing convincing? Will your ideas influence your readers? If not, go back and make the necessary changes.

Sharing

Write your final review in the form of a newspaper article. Write a catchy headline. Paste your article on the front page of an actual newspaper. Cut the newspaper to provide a background for your article and then paste it on a piece of colored art paper. Your teacher will tell you when to share your review with your classmates.

ON YOUR OWN

You may wish to work with a partner on this activity. Choose a book that you both have read. Have one partner write a review of the book, convincing readers that the book is a *must* for everyone to read. Have the other partner write a review that "pans" the book, convincing readers that they should not waste their time reading the book. Use propaganda combined with colorful details from the story that support your point of view. Share your reviews with our classmates. They may be asked to decide which of the reviews is more convincing. In My Word Bank, write four important words you will use in your writing.

My Word Bank

1. _____

2. _____

3. _____

4. _____

Building the Writer's Word Power

A. *Word Pairs*

Writers often use two words to name something. Each word adds something important to the meaning.

spaghetti	raspberry	symphony	permanent	horror	chorus

jam   film   sauce   line   orchestra   press

Match a word from the box with a circled word to form a familiar word pair. Complete each sentence with the word pair that makes the most sense.

1. Children often eat toast with _____

   _____ .

2. There are many fine singers and dancers in a

   _____   _____ .

3. My friend and I were frightened by the _____

   _____ .

4. His aunt plays the violin in a _____

   _____ .

5. You do not need to iron clothing that is _____

   _____ .

6. The chef uses tomatoes to make _____

   _____ .

B. *Anagram Fun*

An anagram is a word made by rearranging the letters of another word. For example, the letters in *tale* can be rearranged to make the word *late*.

Writers who write word games often have fun with anagrams. Write a word from the box and its anagram to complete each sentence.

fringe
spare
siren
crate
cheap
alert

1. The extra weapon the warrior reached for was a

   _____ _____ .

2. How did the workers _____ to the huge size of

   the _____ ?

3. Some _____ guards will be asked to work

   _____ in the day.

4. The customer in the fruit store asked for a _____

   _____ .

5. Use one _____ to hold the

   _____ of the cloth in place.

6. The police officer must _____ the dirt from the

   _____ of her patrol car.

VOCABULARY AND SPELLING

A Picture Is Worth a Thousand Words *Lesson* 28

Draw Me a Picture

When someone explains something to Angela, she often says, "Draw me a picture!" You may have heard this expression before. What Angela is really saying is, "I need more than words to understand what you're saying." Many people, like Angela, need to use pictures such as graphs, charts, or tables to understand some things that writers write about.

Look at this bar graph. Think about the information it provides.

FRIDAY'S MATH TEST SCORES

The bar graph lists not only test scores but also the names of the students who got the scores.

Look at the graph. What do you know about Kirsten? _____

_____

Who got a score of 100? _____

Who got the lowest score? _____

Besides test scores, what are some other facts that writers often show through

the use of graphs? _____

WRITER'S CORNER

Brainstorming
Facts and Graphs

- the average yearly rainfall for five years in a farming region
- the number of teddy bears sold by a toy store in six months
- the number of car accidents caused by speeding during a ten-year period
- in five rounds, the number of times a coin comes up heads in twenty flips of the coin

Writer's Word Bank

1. retreated
2. glimpsed
3. terrified
4. caressed
5. huddled
6. murmured

Planning

Plan a short report that requires a graph to make the facts clear. You may choose one of the topics listed in Facts and Graphs or a topic of your own. (You may use words from the Writer's Word Bank.) You may use a bar graph, a line graph, or a circle graph to show your information. If you were writing a report about average monthly temperatures in New York during 1989, your graph might look like this.

AVERAGE TEMPERATURES IN NEW YORK, 1989

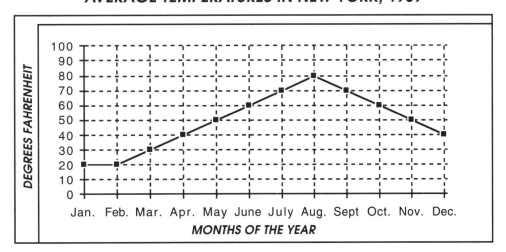

CLUES TO USE

- Writers use graphs to compare amounts and sometimes to show changes over time.
- Good writers use graphs to make their information as clear as possible.

On the lines below, plan your report and the graph that will help make your facts clear.

Writing

On the lines below, write your short report. In the box on the next page, draw the graph.

Editing

Check both your report and graph for accuracy. Does the graph support the facts in your report? Go back and make any necessary changes.

Sharing

Copy your report neatly and mount it on a separate piece of art paper. Add your graph to the art paper. Place the completed report on the class bulletin board for your classmates to read.

ON YOUR OWN

When students write reports, they often include charts. For example a report on trees would be improved if a large chart of a tree and its parts accompanied the report. Choose a science topic. On a separate piece of paper, write a brief report on the topic, no longer than two written pages. Use library resources to help you with your research. Design a chart to accompany your report. Share your finished chart and final report with your classmates. In My Word Bank, write four important words you will use in your writing. (If you need help thinking of an idea to write about, check the Topic Ideas on page 106.)

My Word Bank
1. _____
2. _____
3. _____
4. _____

A Picture Is Worth a Thousand Words *Lesson* **29**

On Schedule

According to Angela, a table doesn't always have four legs. Some tables can be charts that show specific information. One popular kind of table is a schedule. A schedule contains information regarding time and events. Study the bus schedule that follows. What information does it show?

To Los Angeles and San Francisco (all times are P.M.)			
	Bus 71	**Bus 53**	**Bus 44**
leaving San Diego	3:30	4:30	5:30
arriving Santa Ana		6:30	
arriving Disneyland	6:00	7:00	8:00
arriving Los Angeles	7:00	8:00	9:00
arriving San Francisco		12:00	

If a writer wants a character to arrive at Disneyland by 6:30 P.M., which bus would the character take? _____ At what time would the character leave San Diego? _____ .

Good writers work hard to make sure their details are accurate.

The schedule above is a bus schedule. What is one other kind of schedule that some people use every day? _____

GRAPHS, CHARTS, AND TABLES

*W*RITER'S CORNER

Brainstorming
Keep to the Schedule

- daily television programs
- class subjects at school
- activities at a health club
- events at a youth center

Planning

Plan a short article that requires a schedule to help make the information clear. You may use one of the topics in Keep to the Schedule or a topic of your own. The choice is yours. (You may use words from the Writer's Word Bank.)

CLUES TO USE

- A schedule is a table of times and events.
- Some writers use schedules to make times and events clear to the reader.

On the lines below, plan a short article and the schedule that will make the information clear.

_____

_____

_____

_____

_____

_____

_____

_____

_____

_____

GRAPHS, CHARTS, AND TABLES

Writing

On the lines below, write your short article. In the box, write out the schedule that accompanies the article.

_____

_____

_____

_____

_____

_____

_____

_____

GRAPHS, CHARTS, AND TABLES

Editing

Check both your article and schedule. Does the schedule help make the information clear? Have you written the times and events? If not, go back and make the necessary corrections.

Sharing

Copy your finished article and schedule on a large piece of paper. Place your work on the class bulletin board for your classmates to read.

On your own

Choose a social studies or science topic to write a report about. The topic should be one that you are very interested in. Go to the library and find information about your topic. Write down the important facts. Arrange the facts in an order that makes sense. Then draw one or more graphs, charts, or tables that will

My Word Bank
1. _____
2. _____
3. _____
4. _____

help make some of the information clear. Edit your report and write a neat copy of it. Make a large copy of your graph or other visual aid on art paper. Then read your finished report to your classmates and explain the visual aid. In My Word Bank, write four important words you will use in your writing. (If you need help thinking of an idea to write about, check the Topic Ideas on page 106.)

Building the Writer's Word Power

A. *Living Words*

Some writers give human qualities to things that are not human. They do this by writing about these things with words that are ordinarily used when writing about people. Giving human qualities to nonhuman things is called *personification*.

| retreated |
| glimpsed |
| terrified |
| caressed |
| huddled |
| murmured |

Write one word from the box to give human qualities to the subject of each sentence.

1. The bending trees seemed _____ of the raging storm.

2. Large white clouds _____ together in the summer sky.

3. The band of warm weather has _____ to the south.

4. The brook _____ quietly as it flowed through the meadow.

5. The sun _____ at us through the broken clouds.

6. Gentle waves _____ the sandy shore.

B. *IE or EI?*

Writers often have a difficult time dealing with the spelling of *ie* and *ei* words.

grief
foreign
relieve
belief
seize
brief

Write the word from the box that best completes each sentence.

1. Charlie Brown shouted loudly, "Good _____ !"

2. Garfield's humor will temporarily _____ my worries.

3. Superman often battles agents from _____ countries.

4. When did Popeye _____ the crates of spinach?

5. Dennis the Menace gave his mother a _____ rest.

6. "Your conduct is beyond _____ ," Miss Peach told the children.

VOCABULARY AND SPELLING

Appendices—Helpful Tips for Student Writers

TOPIC IDEAS

1. Bigfoot
   (or Other Mysterious Creatures)
2. Updated Nursery Rhymes
3. Aliens from Other Planets
4. Dinosaurs and Animals
   of Long Ago
5. The Pirate's Lost Treasure
6. A Real-Life Adventure
7. The American Revolution
8. An Unsolved Mystery
9. Mountain Climbing in the
   Rockies
10. Baby-sitting for a Brat
11. Writing a Letter to
    a Person in History
12. Living in the City
    (or on a Mountain)
13. Lost in the Woods (or Desert)
14. Fun with My Brother (or Sister)
15. The Best Gift I Ever Gave
    (or Received)
16. A Time I'll Never Forget
17. I Feel Happy When . . .
18. My First Job
19. I Remember When . . .
20. My First Trip to the . . .
21. If I Were a Lion
    (or Any Other Animal)
22. If There Were No TV's, I Would . . .
23. The Greatest Future Invention
    Will Be . .
24. Life in 2010
25. Why People Make Mistakes

26. Why It's Important to Say
    "I'm Sorry!"
27. My Best Friend
28. What I Like About You
29. What I Like About Me
30. Sharing Makes Me Happy
31. What Makes People Hate?
32. The New Kid in Class
33. Changing Schools
34. The World Is Big Enough for
    All Kinds of People
35. If I Had Three Wishes
36. When I Said "Good-bye"
37. An Ideal Vacation
38. Happiness Is . . .
39. What I'll Be Like as an Adult
40. A Summer Camp Adventure
41. I Dream About . . .
42. My Actions Say
    "I Love You" When , . .
43. My Biggest Mistake
44. The Great Diamond Theft
45. The Case of the Mysterious Box
46. White-Water Rafting
47. The Great Forest Fire
48. City Streets (or Country Roads)
49. A Strange Pet
50. My Happiest Moment

WHERE TO FIND TOPIC IDEAS

1. Personal experience
2. Discussions with parents, relatives, and friends
3. People and places around you
4. Neighborhood
5. Diaries
6. Journals
7. Newspapers
8. Magazines
9. Encyclopedias
10. Almanacs
11. Science books
12. Social studies books
13. Library resources
14. Charts and graphs
15. Newsletters
16. Movies
17. Television
18. Videotapes
19. Novels
20. Biographies
21. Cartoons
22. Travel information and guides

SETTING THE SCENE FOR WRITING

Choose a comfortable place.
- A desk or table is a good choice.

Choose a quiet place.
- The writing area should be free of anything that will take your mind off your work.

Gather all your writing materials before you begin.
- You will need such items as paper, pencils, erasers, and a dictionary. You may also need books about your topic.

Stick to the writing job.
- Writing can be difficult work. Sometimes ideas will come to you slowly. Make yourself keep going even when you feel like giving up.

GETTING READY TO WRITE

A Story

- Choose a real or an imaginary person or thing to write about.
- Think of an idea for a plot, or story line.
- Brainstorm for details to develop the plot.
- Decide which details to use and put them in order.

An Article or a Report

- Choose a topic that interests you.
- Gather information about the topic: WHO, WHAT, WHERE, WHEN, and WHY.
- Brainstorm the important facts and how they relate to the topic.
- Put your facts in order.

A Friendly Letter

- Plan to write about people and events that will interest your friend.
- Show interest in the things your friend has been doing.
- Use the standard letter form: heading, greeting, body, closing, and signature.

REVISING YOUR WRITING

When you check your writing, ask the following questions:

1. What did I want to say in my writing?

2. Did I say what I wanted to say?

3. What part of my writing best says what I wanted to say?

4. Have I written clearly enough for others to understand what I wanted to say?

5. What have I done to make my writing interesting to someone else?

6. Is there one main idea in each paragraph?

7. Do I have details and examples that tell enough about my main idea?

8. Are my ideas written in an order that is clear?

PROOFREADING YOUR WRITING

When you proofread your writing, ask the following questions:

1. Do all my sentences make sense?

2. Did I use a capital letter at the beginning of every sentence?

3. Did I use a capital letter for all names?

4. Did I use correct punctuation marks?

5. Are all the words spelled correctly? (Check words you are not sure of.)

6. Did I indent the first word of each paragraph?

Editing Symbols

¶ indent	∧ add	/ lowercase
≡ use a capital	ℓ take out	

Sample:

¶ When ann goes to the store, she she looks for toy dinosaurs.
She has red ones, Green ones, big ones, and little ones.